THE ELEPHANT BOOK

A book about Elephants . . .

Their hopes, fears, jokes

and psychological problems

PRICE / STERN / SLOAN
Publishers, Inc., Los Angeles
1974

WHEN YOU HAVE AN ELEPHANT BY THE HIND LEG
AND HE'S TRYING TO RUN AWAY,
IT'S BEST TO LET HIM RUN—

Abraham Lincol n

18th Printing — October 1974

Copyright © 1963, 1964, 1968, 1972 by Price/Stern/Sloan Publishers, Inc.
410 North La Cienega Boulevard, Los Angeles, California 90048
Printed in the United States of America. All Rights Reserved.
Library of Congress Catalog Card No.: 63-24730
ISBN: 0-8431-0010-9

TONS OF PUBLICITY and advertising have been devoted to detergents, Pakistan, monosodium glutamate, Barbra Streisand, pizza, Ted Kennedy, panty hose, Asian flu, Burt Reynolds and toothpaste. But is anything really more deserving of recognition than the Elephant?

Can Pakistan squirt water through its nose?

Can Burt Reynolds eat 285 pounds of peanuts in a single day? Perhaps, but it's doubtful.

The following collection of Vital Elephant Information has been compiled and written* by Lennie Weinrib — along with Roger Price, Leonard Stern and Larry Sloan — in an attempt to correct this gross injustice.

Remember, the Elephant is Man's Best *Big* Friend.

The splendid decorations of Elephants in this book are by their friend, Ed Powers.

What did Tarzan say when he saw the elephants coming over the hill?

"Here come the elephants over the hill."

What did Tarzan say when he saw the elephants coming over the hill wearing dark glasses?

Nothing, he didn't recognize them.

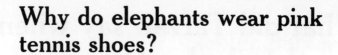

Why do elephants wear pink tennis shoes?

Because white ones get dirty too fast.

Why do elephants float down the river on their backs?

So they won't get their tennis shoes wet.

Why do elephants have wrinkled ankles?

Because their tennis shoes are too tight.

Why do elephants have wrinkled knees?

From playing marbles.

How do you tell an elephant from a grape?

A grape is purple.

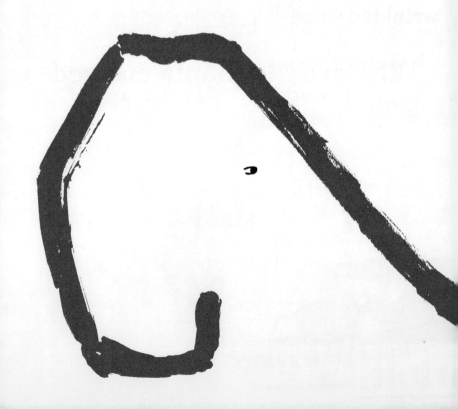

What did Jane say when she saw the elephants?

"OOH look at all those grapes." (She was colorblind.)

Why are elephants colored grey?

So you can tell them from canaries.

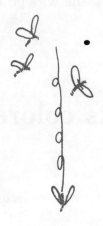

What is it that looks like an elephant and flies?

A flying elephant.

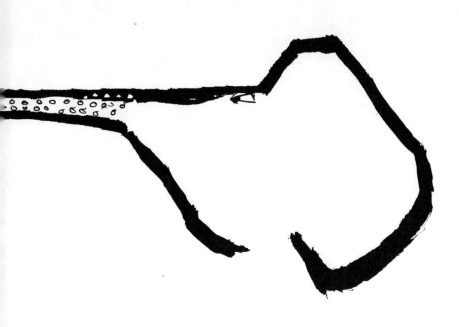

What is it that looks like an elephant and flies and is very dangerous?

A flying elephant with a machine gun.

If you're colorblind how do you tell an elephant from a grape?

Jump around on it for awhile. If you don't get any wine it's an elephant.

Why don't more elephants go to college?

Not too many elephants finish high school.

How do you put six elephants in a Volkswagen?

Three in front and three in back . . .

Why do elephants need trunks?

Because they don't have glove compartments.

Why do elephants have flat feet?

From jumping out of trees.

How do you know if an elephant's standing near you in an elevator?

By the smell of peanuts on his breath.

Why do elephants prefer peanuts to caviar?

Because they're easier to get at the ballpark.

How does an elephant put his trunk in a crocodile's mouth?

VERY carefully.

What do you call elephants who ride on trains?

Passengers.

Why do girl elephants wear angora sweaters?

So you can tell them from boy elephants.

What does a bald elephant wear for a toupee?

A sheep.

Why don't elephants like blue lace petticoats?

Who said they don't like blue lace petticoats ? ? ?

Where do baby elephants come from?

BIG storks.

What did the banana say to the elephant?

Nothing, bananas can't talk.

Why do elephants lie on their backs with their feet in the air?

So they

can

trip birds.

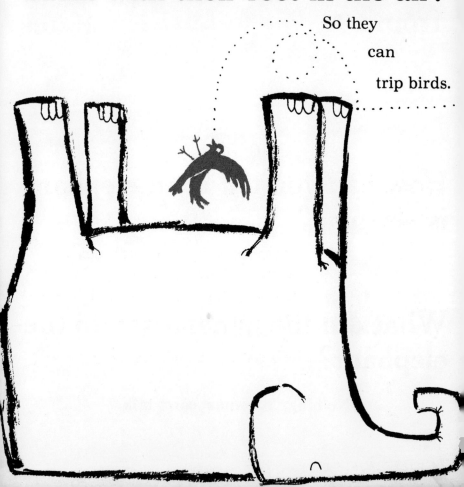

How can you tell if an elephant is sleeping?

When he's in bed with the
covers pulled up and
he's wearing pajamas and
his pink tennis shoes are off,
the chances are
he's asleep, if he's snoring.

But watch it anyway.

Why did the elephant walk around in polka-dot socks?

Somebody stole his tennis shoes.

Why did the elephants quit their job at the factory?

They got tired of working for peanuts.

How do you housebreak an elephant?

You get 14 copies of the New York Times—the Sunday edition.

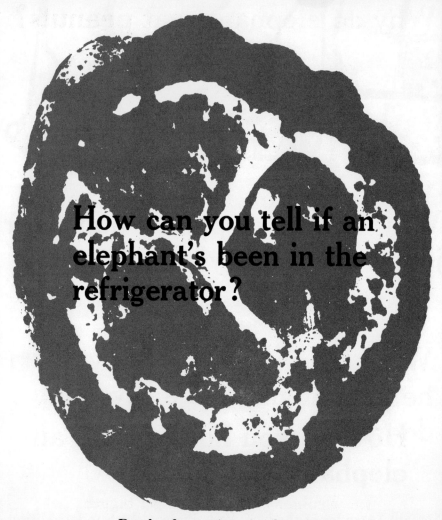

How can you tell if an elephant's been in the refrigerator?

By the footprints in the pizza.

Why do elephants eat peanuts?

Because **they're saltier** than prunes.

Where do you find elephants?

It depends where you lost them.

What did the elephant say when he got caught in the revolving door?

" If this place wants to do much business with elephants, they better get bigger revolving doors!"

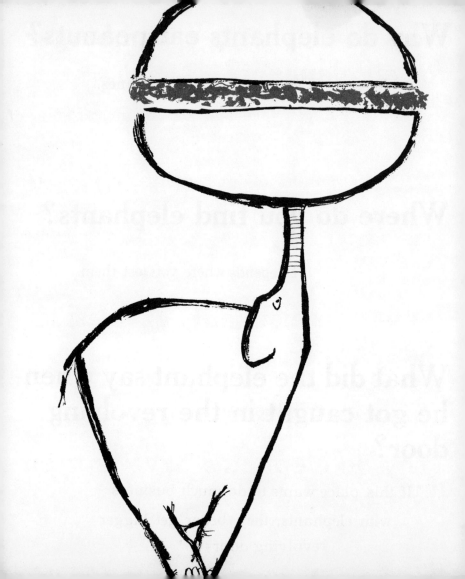

How do you make a hamburger for an elephant?

First you take 500 jars of mustard,
60 gallons of catsup,
90 pounds of onions,
and then you get this BIG roll . . .

What do elephants eat beside hamburgers?

Canned elephant food.

Why do elephants have hair on their tails?

Why not?

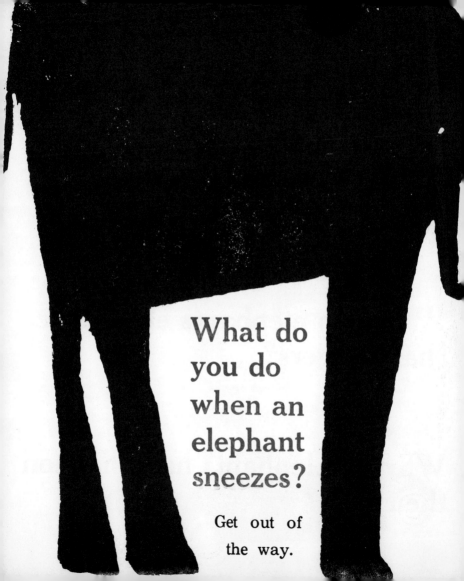

What do
you do
when an
elephant
sneezes?

Get out of
the way.

What did the nearsighted elephant say when the Volkswagen ran into it?

"How many times have I told you kids
—don't play in the street!"

Why don't elephants ride busses during rush hour?

They're afraid of pickpockets.

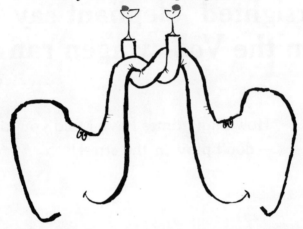

What does an elephant smell like before it takes a shower?

An elephant.

What does an elephant smell like after it takes a shower?

A wet elephant.

How many elephants on a Nurndy team?

Ten. Two borks, six forwards and two wopplers.

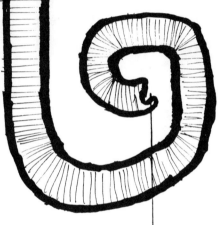

Why are elephants so much better at Nurndy than people?

Because they wopple better.

Why don't elephants like martinis?

Did you ever try to get an olive out of your nose?

Why aren't more elephants called Walter?

Because Ed and Norm are better names for elephants.

How does an elephant get out of a phone booth?

The same way he got in.

What did the nearsighted elephant say when he saw the
tank? "Hi pop."

What do you call a hippopotamus who's been carrying
elephants across the river
all day?

A VERY tired hippopotamus.

What did Jane say when she saw the elephant working in the drug store?

"I didn't know the giraffe sold the place!"

Which elephants don't get toothaches?

Those in the half of the herd that uses Crest.

How much wood would a woodchuck chuck if a woodchuck could chuck wood?

Listen, you want to know about woodchucks, get the Woodchuck Book. This is The Elephant Book.

What did Tarzan say when he saw the male elephant jump off the cliff?

"That's how the big bull bounces."

How do you get an elephant out of a tub of gelatin?

Follow the directions on the back of the box.

What is this elephant doing?

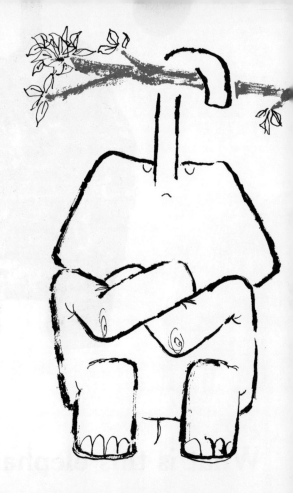

Making a monkey out of himself.

Why do elephants live in the jungle?

Because it's out of the high rent district.

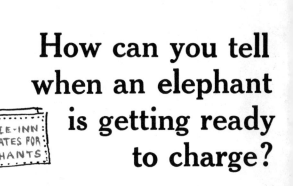

JUNGLE-INN
LOW RATES FOR
ELEPHANTS

How can you tell when an elephant is getting ready to charge?

He takes out his Diner's Club card.

What did the elephant say to the maharajah?

"Get off my back."

Why do elephants jump across rivers?

So they won't step on the fish.

Why does an elephant never forget?

What's he got to remember?

Does an elephant have to
remember where he parked his car,
or his wedding anniversary,
or if he left the water running
in the basement?

What did the elephants say when they saw Tarzan leaving the jungle?

"There goes Tarzan leaving the jungle."
Except for one tiny little elephant
who ran out
in
front
and
said
"Goodbye."

SOME FURTHER QUESTIONS ABOUT ELEPHANTS THAT HAVE NOT AT THIS POINT BEEN ANSWERED:

Why aren't there more Elephants in the Space Program?

Why has the Elephant been replaced as a Household Pet by the Cat?

Why do Rhinoceroses get all the good parts in Westerns?

Not one Elephant has been invited to Buckingham Palace in the past six months. Why is this?

Why isn't the CIA training Elephants in Guatemala?

What is the Mayor of Waterloo, Iowa, doing about the Elephant question?

When was the last time you took an Elephant to lunch?

This book is published by
PRICE / STERN / SLOAN
Publishers, Inc., Los Angeles

Whose other splendid titles include
such literary classics as:
Elephants, Grapes and Pickles
The Monster Joke Book
The World's Worst Jokes
The Mad Libs Series
Designs to Color Series
and many, many more.
They are available wherever books are sold or
may be ordered directly from the publisher.
For complete list write:

PRICE / STERN / SLOAN *Publishers, Inc.*

410 North La Cienega Boulevard
Los Angeles, California 90048